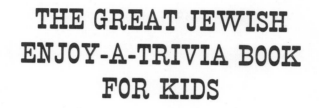

THE GREAT JEWISH ENJOY-A-TRIVIA BOOK FOR KIDS

Written by kids for kids!!

Illustrated by Linda Holland Rathkopf

Simcha Publishing Co., Inc.
25 Lawrence Ave.
Lawrence, N.Y. 11559

ISBN: 0-943706-06-8

Also available from Simcha Publishing Co.

ZEYDEH
THE ADVENTURES OF SIMCHA THE SEAL
SIMCHA SAVES THE SHATTERED SHABBAT
THE SIMCHA COLORING/ACTIVITY BOOKS
THE CHANUKAH FUN BOOK
THE ALEF-BET COLORING/ACTIVITY BOOK

A L.I.F.E. Publication

Dedicated to the beloved memory of

JOSEPH PETERSEIL
"The Candy Man"

He sweetened the lives of thousands of children in shul, who took candy from his hands and love from his heart.

His memory will endure in them and in us.

Esther Peterseil

Yaacov and Dorothy

Tehila, Gedalia, Shlomo,
Zoe, Nachum, Tiferet and Jo Beth

HOW

"THE GREAT JEWISH ENJOY-A-TRIVIA BOOK FOR KIDS"

CAME TO BE:

A True Story

The idea for a Jewish kids trivia book came about during a brainstorming session at the offices of Enjoy-A-Book Club, the Jewish Childrens' book club. All of us were huddled around a desk, excited about the prospect of publishing a book filled with Jewish facts for kids. It was only when the question of what to call such a book came up that disharmony reared its ugly head among our small band of Jewish book mavens. A still, small voice (we were never able to determine who it was) suggested that we call our book, **THE GREAT JEWISH ENJOY-A-TRIVIA BOOK FOR KIDS.**

Silence settled like a heavy chulent among us.

"Blasphemy!" shouted one of our number, aghast at the thought that we would ever consider Jewish facts on the same footing with run-of-the-mill-non-Jewish trivia. How dare we, went the argument, equate the sanctity of Jewish Life and Jewish Thought with the mundane and, indeed, trivial aspects of everyday existence. If anything, such a book as we propose should be called **THE GREAT JEWISH ENJOY-AN-UNTRIVIA BOOK FOR KIDS,** to counteract even the suggestion that Jewish facts might be unimportant or trivial.

"Borscht!" yelled another of our compatriots, pressing the argument that the word "trivia", when applied to Jewish facts, aptly reflects the attitude of the vast majority of Jewish children who have no interest in Jewish history, philosophy or religion, despite a modest Hebrew School education. For them, Jewish facts are of little or no consequence to their day-to-day lives. Indeed, by reading our "trivia" book these kids may be inspired to read and learn a little bit more about their Jewish heritage.

"Death to Darth Vader!" I screamed, for no other reason than to get their attention, which it did. "Consider the toad", I continued, to the boos and hisses of my comrades, "or would you rather be fired?" I concluded, amid stunned silence and clear reverence for my next words.

I then proceeded to explain that our goal in publishing this book was to teach kids about Judaism. In this we were all agreed. But, in order to accomplish our goal we would first have to get kids to pick up our book, even at the expense of using a faddish, popular term, "trivia," to describe an eternal, uncompromising truth: Judaism. In short, **THE GREAT JEWISH ENJOY-A-TRIVIA BOOK FOR KIDS** would be a vehicle to help kids reach the conclusion, by themselves, that Jewish trivia is really un-trivia of the highest order.

With no dissenting opinion on the horizon (who would dare), I next suggested that the best method for gathering questions and answers for our book would be a contest. Kids across the country would have an opportunity to send in questions which we might use in our book. The winners would, of course, receive special prizes.

100,000 applications outlining the rules of **THE GREAT JEWISH ENJOY-A-TRIVIA BOOK FOR KIDS** contest were sent as part of our next bi-monthly Enjoy-A-Book Club brochure. Within 4 weeks, over 3,000 questions and answers found their way to our offices in Woodmere, New York. After months of sifting through these decidedly non-trivial questions, the winners were selected. They are:

Shmuel Theiner, Pittsburg, PA. — GRAND PRIZE WINNER
Meryl Kaplan, Fort Worth, TX. — BIBLE
Aaron Meadow, Larchmont, NY. — JEWISH HOLIDAYS
Chaia Wald, Far Rockaway, NY. — ARTS AND LITERATURE
Aida Radfar, Flossmoor, IL. — CUSTOMS AND LAW
Michelle Kwitkin, Plainview, NY. — HEBREW LANGUAGE
Jonathan Novich, St. Paul, MN. — JEWISH GEOGRAPHY
Michael Gutterman, Oxford, OH. — FAMOUS JEWISH MEN AND WOMEN
Devorah Schechter, New York, NY. — MY JEWISH NAME MEANS ...

During a secret board meeting at Enjoy-A-Book Club world headquarters, (Post Office Box 101, Woodmere, NY), it was decided to list all the contestants, by way of saying thank you for their interest and hard work. Their parents and teachers should be proud of them, as we all are.

One final word. **THE GREAT JEWISH ENJOY-A-TRIVIA BOOK FOR KIDS** is the product of a small, dedicated staff of unique (some have said, strange) individuals. Shimon Spirn, our Executive Vice-Everything, managed to collect and edit all the questions and answers while simultaneously juggling no less than eight different projects we were working on at the same time. Of course, he still managed to ship all Enjoy-A-Book Club orders on time. Shlomo Berger, Sales Manager Extraordinaire, sold us on the idea of a Jewish trivia book with his enthusiasm and verbal vociferousness. His ideas and comments were always on the mark. Jane Shapiro, Project Coordinator For Special Projects And Anything New, was the sounding board and yardstick by which we were able to judge the potential effectiveness of each question for our perceived audience. Ingrid Wald, Untitled, collated and typed the final draft (and every draft in-between), adding her own special "why not try this" touch to the project.

To all of them a hearty Yashar Koach for a job well done.

Yaacov Peterseil
June 21, 1985
2 Tammuz, 5745

CONTRIBUTORS

Abbouline, Yehuda	Brooklyn, NY
Arking, Moshe	Brooklyn, NY
Baran, Adam	Sioux Falls, SD
Baran, David	Sioux Falls, SD
Baltuch, Robin	North Miami Beach, FL
Bergman, Akiva	Lawrence, NY
Berney, Kerry	Morganville, NJ
Bien-Willner, Carol	Paradise Valley, AZ
Block, Marla	Brooklyn, NY
Born, Lonny Jay	Paradise Valley, AZ
Brafman, Esther	Far Rockaway, NY
Brafman, Rena	Far Rockaway, NY
Buendo, Robin	Longmeadow, MA
Chatlynne, Etan	Sioux Falls, SD
Cline, Heather	Randolph, MA
Davidsohn, Sharon	Sioux Falls, SD
DuMone, William	Paradise Valley, AZ
Eisen, Rachel	Laurel Springs, NJ
Elefant, Daniel	Corvallis, OR
Engelhart, Lauren	Somerset, NJ
Ever, Isaac	Miami Beach, FL
Fisher, Jonathan Michael	Somerset, NJ
Frank, Shelly	Sioux Falls, SD
Gantner, Erica	Reynoldsburg, OH
Gilbert, Beth	Coran, NY
Golombeck, Yehudis	Philadelphia, PA
Gordon, Matthew Frederick	Paradise Valley, AZ
Green, Jared	Fayetteville, NC
Gutkin, Benjamin Tzvi	Paradise Valley, AZ
Gutt, Michelle	Raleigh, NC
Gutterman, Michael	Oxford, OH
Hack, Mara	Ridgeway, MI
Harel, Yahel	Pittsburg, PA
Hegna, Gretchen	Sioux Falls, SD
Hirsch, Kerri	Paradise Valley, AZ
Jacobs, Aviva	Silver Springs, MD
Kaplan, Hyla	Barrington, RI
Kaplan, Meryl	Fort Worth, TX
Karas, Julie	Swampscott, MA
Kittredge, Michael	Longmeadow, MA
Klapper, Jennie	Dallas, TX
Klein, Abraham Dov	Berkeley, CA
Kluger, Jacob	Phoenix, AZ
Kochin, Ethlyn	Seattle, WA
Koffler, Allison	Somerset, NJ
Kolonder, Jonnie	Oldsmar, FL
Kraushaar, Dabra	Gillette, WY
Kraushaar, Steve	Gillette, WY
Kunstantyn, Ariel	East Meadow, NY
Kwitkin, Michelle	Plainview, NY
Lampel, Ryan	Scottsdale, AZ
Landesman, Heather	Wheeling, MI
Langer, Naomi	Belfort, NJ
Levenbaum, Ari Seth	Paradise Valley, AZ

Levitsky, Lily	New York, NY
Liberman, Shifra	Chicago, IL
Lipovitch, Suzanne	Paradise Valley, AZ
Litman, Cheryl	Oceanside, NY
Mannis, Avi	Sacramento, CA
Margolis, Ari	Bowie, MD
Marx, Joshua	Piscataway, NJ
Mausel, David	Longmeadow, MA
Meadow, Aaron	Larchmont, NY
Mendelsohn, David	Sioux Falls, SD
Mendelsohn, Jessica	Sioux Falls, SD
Meranus, Stacy	Pine Brook, NJ
Metzger, Janie	Sioux Falls, SD
Miller, Anne	Tuscon, AZ
Novich, Jonathan	St. Paul, MN
Ofstein, Charlie	Sioux Falls, SD
Ofstein, Ricky	Sioux Falls, SD
Padwe, Melissa	Scottsdale, AZ
Peterseil, Gedalia	Lawrence, NY
Peterseil, Tehila	Lawrence, NY
Peterseil, Shlomo	Lawrence, NY
Radfar, Aida	Flossmoor, IL
Raphael, Miriam	Seattle, WA
Rasis, Dana	St. Louis, MO
Rosenthal, Harry	Sioux Falls, SD
Rosenthal, Jackie	Sioux Falls, SD
Rosenthal, Jordana	Somerset, NJ
Sandberg, Devora	Brooklyn, NY
Schechter, Devorah	New York, NY
Schotten, Cheryl	Sioux Falls, SD
Sher, Bradley David	Paradise Valley, AZ
Sloane, Richard Neil	Paradise Valley, AZ
Stahl, David	Larchmont, NY
Stein, Aharon	West Hempstead, NY
Stein, David	West Hempstead, NY
Stein, Meier	West Hempstead, NY
Steiner, Herschel	Merion, PA
Tash, Sloan Murray	Scottsdale, AZ
Theiner, Shmuel	Pittsburgh, PA
Thompson, Jeremy	Chelmsford, MA
Thorpe, Leslie Renee	Paradise Valley, AZ
Thrope, Jessica	Sioux Falls, SD
Torrico, Erick	Dallas, TX
Wand, Jordan	Dix Hills, NY
Wald, Avi Joseph	Far Rockaway, NY
Wald, Chaia Rochel	Far Rockaway, NY
Weber, Ari Joseph	Paradise Valley, AZ
Weinman, Jennifer	Fort Worth, TX
Weiss, Shimmy	Southfield, MI
Wellerstein, Jaimee	Paradise Valley, AZ
Weil, Brian Scott	Richton Park, IL
Yablon, Alyse	Philadelphia, PA
Yariv, Eden	

FAMOUS JEWISH MEN AND WOMEN

1. Which Jew was a financial consultant to 4 presidents of the USA?

2. The Arabs trace their ancestry to which Biblical character?

3. Who was the Jewish advisor to King Ferdinand and Queen Isabella?

4. What Jewish heroine left Palestine to parachute behind German lines in Hungary?

5. Where was Golda Meir born?

6. Name the Jewish woman astronaut on the shuttle "Discovery"?

ANSWERS:

1. Bernard Baruch
2. Ishmael
3. Isaac Abarbanel
4. Hannah Senesh
5. Kiev, Russia
6. Judith A. Resnick

1. To whom is the discovery of the Polio Vaccine credited?

2. Who started and coached the Harlem Globetrotters?

3. Who invented the Polaroid Land Camera?

4. Who wrote the poem on the Statue of Liberty?

5. Who was known as the "Little Champ"?

6. Which Jewish baseball player knew 12 languages?

1. Dr. Jonas Salk and Dr. Albert Sabin
2. Abe Saperstein
3. Edwin Land
4. Emma Lazarus
5. Abe Attell
6. Morris Berg (Moe)

1. Who was the only Jewish boxing champion who refused to fight on a Jewish holiday?

2. Who was the only man to ever pitch two shutouts in a double header?

3. Who was known as the quarterback who "never made a mistake"?

4. Which football player was known as the "Rabbi?

5. Who was the only Jew ever to win at Wimbleton?

6. Who was known as the "Jewish Babe Ruth"?

1. Benny Leonard
2. Edward Reulbach
3. Sid Luckman
4. Randy Grossman
5. Richard Savitt
6. Andy Cohen

1. Who founded the Chassidic movement?

2. Who founded the Zionist movement?

3. Which famous Jewish girl won a beauty contest and half a kingdom?

4. What do Isaac Stern, Yasha Heifetz and Yitzchak Perlman have in common?

5. Which famous Jewish comedian gets "no respect"?

1. The Ba'al Shem Tov
2. Theodore Herzl
3. Esther
4. They are all great violinists.
5. Rodney Dangerfield

1. Where was Rashi born?

2. Who was the only Jewish commodore of the U.S. Navy?

3. Name 3 justices of the Supreme Court who were Jewish?

4. Who was the major financier of the American Revolution?

5. Who compiled the Shulchan Aruch?

6. Who discovered the Theory of Relativity?

1. Troyes, France
2. Uriah P. Levy
3. Brandeis, Cardoza, Goldberg, Frankfurter, Fortas
4. Haym Solomon
5. Joseph Caro
6. Albert Einstein

1. In which century did Reb. Samson Raphael Hirsch live?

2. Which crime was Alfred Dreyfus charged with?

3. Who was called the "second Moses"?

4. Who was known as the "hunchback who enlightened the Jews"?

5. Who was the founder of the House of Rothschild?

1. 19th
2. Treason
3. Moses Maimonides
4. Moses Mendelsohn
5. Mayer Anscholl Rothschild

1. Who was the second King of Israel?

2. Who was Abraham's nephew?

3. Who is buried in Herzl's tomb?

4. Name the first president of Israel?

5. How many medals did Mark Spitz win in the 1973 Olympics?

6. Which evil practice did the Chofetz Chaim preach against?

1. David
2. Lot
3. Theodore Herzl
4. Chaim Weitzman
5. Seven
6. Loshon Hora (speaking evil)

1. Who was Naomi's daughter-in-law besides Ruth?

2. Which sage did not study Torah until the age of 40?

3. What does the acronym "Rambam" stand for?

4. Who wrote the "Great Jewish Enjoy-A-Trivia Book for Kids"?

5. Who was born Allen Stewart Koenigsberg?

6. What controversial Jewish sports announcer was born with the name Howard Cohen?

1. Orpah
2. Rabbi Akiva
3. Rabbi Moses ben Maimon
4. Kids
5. Woody Allen
6. Howard Cosell

1. What Jewish tough-guy actor was born with the name Charles Buchinsky?

2. What Jew is the world's most famous mime?

3. Which University is named after a famous Jewish Supreme Court Justice?

4. Whose stained glass windows depict the 12 tribes?

5. Which 5 brothers made funny movies in the '30's and '40's?

1. Charles Bronson
2. Marcel Marceau
3. Brandeis University
4. Marc Chagall
5. The Marx Brothers

1. Which famous non-Jew helped save thousands of Hungarian Jews?

2. Who is the only Jewish-born Prime Minister of Great Britain?

3. Who was the first Chief Rabbi of Israel?

4. Which famous British Lord wore a kipah?

5. Who founded the Jewish Defense League?

1. Who was the first female Prime Minister of Israel?

2. Who was the only Jewish Miss America?

3. Name two Biblical prophetesses?

4. What was Bar Kochba's other name?

5. Who is the father of the American Nuclear Navy?

6. Which Hungarian Jew is the father of the H-bomb?

1. Golda Meir
2. Bess Meyerson
3. Devorah and Miriam
4. Bar Kosiba
5. Admiral Hyman Rickover
6. Edward Teller

1. Who was the first Prime Minister of Israel?

2. Who is the mayor of Jerusalem?

3. Who was the youngest Olympic athlete to win the Gold Medal?

4. Who was the youngest baseball player ever to be admitted into the Baseball Hall of Fame?

5. Which Jewish woman doctor won a Nobel Prize for her medical research?

6. Who founded Hadassah?

1. David ben Gurion
2. Teddy Kollak
3. Jackie Fields
4. Sandy Koufax
5. Rosalind Yalow
6. Henrietta Szold

1. Who was the only Jewish Secretary of State in the United States?

2. Who wrote "Hatikvah"?

3. After the destruction of the Temple who was the founder of the Yeshivah at Yavneh?

4. Who was the greatest Jewish leader and law giver?

5. What is Sholom Aleichem's real name?

1. Henry Kissinger
2. Naphtali Hertz Imber
3. Yochanan ben Zakkai
4. Moses
5. Shlomo Rabinowitz

BIBLE

1. How many days was Moses on Mount Sinai?

2. Who was the first Jew?

3. What is the third commandment?

4. Who tricked Eve into eating from the "forbidden tree"?

5. How many plagues were visited upon the Egyptians?

6. Which mountain did Noah's ark land on?

7. Where did Adam and Eve live?

ANSWERS:
1. 40
2. Avraham
3. Don't take G-d's name in vain
4. The evil serpent (snake)
5. 10
6. Mount Ararat
7. Garden of Eden

1. Name Adam and Eve's third son?

2. Name the five books of Moses?

3. How many days did it rain during the flood?

4. Who wore the coat of many colors?

5. Who was Jacob's youngest son?

6. Who was Moses' sister?

7. In which river was Moses found?

1. Seth
2. Genesis, Exodus, Leviticus, Numbers and Deuteronomy
3. 40
4. Joseph
5. Benjamin
6. Miriam
7. Nile

1. Which body of water did Moses separate?

2. Which tribe did Moses belong to?

3. Name the ten plagues?

4. Whom did Moses appoint to take over for him?

5. Who killed Goliath?

6. How was Goliath killed?

7. Was Miriam older or younger than Moses?

1. The Red Sea
2. Levi
3. Blood, frogs, lice, wild animals, cattle disease, boils, hail, locusts, darkness, death of the firstborn.
4. Joshua
5. David
6. With a stone from his slingshot.
7. Older

1. Who were Adam and Eve's first 2 sons?

2. What did Cain say to G-d after he killed Abel?

3. What was Moses' father-in-law's name?

4. Who was Moses' wife?

5. The Israelites created what graven image in the desert?

6. How many Psalms are there in the Book of Psalms?

1. Cain and Abel
2. "Am I my brother's keeper?"
3. Jethro
4. Zipporah
5. Golden Calf
6. 150 Psalms

1. How many spies did Moses send into Canaan?

2. Who was Joshua's father?

3. What were the names of Isaac's two sons?

4. Who was Ishmael's mother?

5. What two things did the matriarchs Rachel and Leah have in common?

6. What title was given to the King of Egypt?

1. 12
2. Nun
3. Jacob and Esau
4. Hagar
5. Same father (Laban); same husband (Jacob)
6. Pharoh

1. Who came first in the Torah, Abraham or Noah?

2. Name Noah's three sons.

3. Name Moses' two sons.

4. What are the names of the four matriarchs?

5. How much was Joseph worth to his brothers?

6. In which city did the Jews in Egypt live before the Exodus?

1. Noah
2. Ham, Shem, Japeth
3. Gershon and Eliezer
4. Sarah, Rebecca, Rachel and Leah
5. 30 pieces of silver
6. Goshen

1. Who was the only daughter of Jacob?

2. Who were the parents of Moses?

3. What king threw Daniel into the lion's den?

4. What guided the children of Israel through the desert by day?

5. What is the first commandment in the Torah?

6. What name did Pharoh give to Joseph?

1. Dinah
2. Amram and Yocheved
3. Darius
4. "A pillar of cloud"
5. Be fruitful and multiply
6. Tzafnat Paneach

1. Who lived longer than anyone else in the Bible?

2. Who is the only person whose birthday is mentioned in the Torah?

3. In what two chapters of the Torah are the 10 commandments mentioned?

4. What did the Ark of the Covenant contain?

5. Where is our matriarch, Sarah, buried?

6. Who adopted Moses?

1. Methuselah
2. Pharoh
3. Jethro and V'Etchanon
4. The original 10 tablets
5. The Cave of Machpellah
6. Pharoh's daughter

1. Which song did the Jews sing when they crossed the Red Sea?

2. How many stops did the Jews make going from Egypt to Mount Sinai?

3. How many portions are there in the Torah?

4. How many children did Abraham have?

5. How many sons did Jacob have?

6. What was Moses' punishment for hitting the rock?

1. Az Yashir
2. 11
3. 54
4. 11 (from three wives)
5. 12
6. He could not enter the Land of Israel

1. Name the five Megillot?

2. How did Haman decide the fate of the Jews?

3. Who said "Thy people shall be my people, Thy G-d, my G-d."?

4. How many years did Adam live?

5. Abraham sacrificed which animal instead of Isaac?

6. For how many years did the Jews slave in Egypt?

7. How many commandments are mentioned in the Torah?

1. Esther, Song of Songs, Ruth, Lamentations, Ecclesiastes
2. He drew lots
3. Ruth to Naomi
4. 930 years
5. Ram
6. 210
7. 613

1. Who was the first King of Israel?

2. Who built the first Temple?

3. What caused the walls of Jericho to fall?

4. How old was Moses when he died?

5. How many daughters did Jethro have?

6. Who was saved from the destruction at Jericho?

7. Who killed Cain?

1. Saul
2. Solomon
3. Shofar blast
4. 120
5. 7
6. Rachov
7. Lemech

JEWISH HOLIDAYS

1. How many candles are lit on the first day of Chanukah?

2. Name the special fruit you eat on Tu B'Shevat?

3. Which holiday is King Antiochus associated with?

4. During which major holiday is one prohibited from eating?

5. Name at least three national fast days?

6. How many days did the oil last in the original Chanukah menorah?

1. Name the villain in the Purim Megillah?

2. What is the name of the holiday which celebrates the finishing of the reading of the Torah?

3. Which fast day falls just before Purim?

4. Which letter is different on the American dreidles than on the Israeli dreidles?

5. On which holiday do we search for the Afikoman?

1. Haman
2. Simchat Torah
3. Fast of Esther
4. The American dreidle has a shin (there) and the Israeli dreidle has a pey (here).
5. Passover

1. In which town does the story of Chanukah take place?

2. What is the name of the unleavened bread we eat on Passover?

3. What is the Hebrew term for the search of leaven the night before Passover?

4. In which direction do you light the Chanukah menorah?

5. Which language is the Kol Nidre prayer written in?

1. Modin
2. Matzoh
3. Bedikat Chometz
4. From left to right
5. Aramaic

1. How many cups of wine must we drink at the Seder on Passover?

2. On which fast day is the "Book of Lamentations" ("KINOT") read?

3. On which holiday do we eat "maror"?

4. In Israel, what is the name of the special jelly donut eaten on Chanukah?

5. What is the age of Bar Mitzvah?

6. What does Passover mean?

1. 4 cups
2. Tisha B'Av
3. Passover
4. Sofganiot
5. 13 years
6. To pass over

1. Hadassah is another name for which Purim Queen?

2. Why does a Sukkah not require a mezuzah?

3. What is Yom Yerushalayim?

4. Name at least three foods on the Seder plate?

5. What is the custom of giving someone a present on Purim called?

6. Name at least two events which occurred on the 9th of Av?

1. Esther
2. Because it is a temporary, not a permanent, dwelling.
3. The day Jerusalem was unified
4. Maror, Karpas, Chazeret, Charoses, Zeroa, Baytzah
5. Shalach Manot
6. a) Destruction of the First Temple
   b) Destruction of the Second Temple
   c) Expulsion of the Jews from Spain

1. On which holiday does a child recite the "Ma Nishtanah?"

2. What is the Hebrew date on which Chanukah occurs?

3. On which three holidays did Jews travel to Jerusalem?

4. On which holiday is it customary to stay up all night and learn Torah?

5. What is the Hebrew word for "New Year of the Trees"?

1. Passover
2. 25th day of Kislev
3. Passover, Sukkot and Shavuot
4. Shavuot
5. Tu B'Shevat

1. What happened on Shavuot?

2. What is another name for Rosh Chodesh?

3. Achashverosh ruled how many provinces?

4. How many times is the Megillah read on Purim?

5. How many sons did Haman have?

6. Name the two heroes of the Purim Megillah?

1. G-d gave Moses the ten Commandments
2. New moon
3. 127
4. Twice
5. 10
6. Esther and Mordechai

1. How many Matzohs are needed at the Seder table?

2. How many sons are mentioned in the Hagaddah?

3. An etrog is held on which holiday?

4. What is the name given to the last day of Sukkot?

5. In how many directions do we shake the etrog and lulav?

6. How many brothers did Judah the Maccabee have?

1. What is the fifth cup of wine at the Passover Seder for?

2. What is the name of the piece of Matzoh that children hide on Passover?

3. What is another name for Chanukah money?

4. The Maccabees fought against which Syrian king?

5. Which song is sung after lighting the Chanukah candles?

6. What is another name for the Greeks of the Maccabee period?

1. Elijah's cup
2. Afikoman
3. Chanukah Gelt
4. Antiochus
5. Maoz Tzur (Rock of Ages)
6. Hellenists

ARTS

AND

LITERATURE

1. Name the museum in Jerusalem dedicated as a memorial to the victims of the holocaust?

2. On what famous American object is the verse from Leviticus "Proclaim liberty throughout the land" written?

3. What famous Yiddish writer received the Nobel Prize for Literature?

4. What is the national anthem of Israel?

1. Who wrote "The Chosen"?

2. Who was the evil Jewish character in Dickens' "Oliver Twist"?

3. What was Tevye's profession in "Fiddler on the Roof"?

4. Who is the only Israeli to win the Nobel Prize in Literature?

5. Who is the Jewish Mark Twain?

6. Who is the Jewish reporter who teamed up with Bob Woodward to expose Watergate?

1. Chaim Potok
2. Fagan
3. Milkman
4. S. Y. Agnon
5. Sholom Aleichem
6. Carl Bernstein

1. What famous artist painted Moses holding the two tablets?

2. What are the 6 orders of the Mishnah?

3. Who wrote the "Carp in the Bathtub"?

4. Who wrote the "Adventures of Ktonton"?

5. How many times is the word "hava" used in the song "Hava Nagila?"

1. Name the Orthodox Jewish American author who wrote "The Caine Mutiny" and "This is my G-d" among many other books?

2. The prayer "Yigdal" is based upon the *13 Principles of Faith* outlined by which famous Jewish philosopher?

3. What was the other name of Saadya ben Joseph, the author of the book "Beliefs and Opinions"?

4. The wise men of Chelm are really very _____?

1. Herman Wouk
2. Moses Maimonides
3. Saadya Gaon
4. Naïve or funny

1. Name the successful cantor who became an opera star?

2. "Death of a Salesman" was written by which famous Jewish Pulitzer Prize winning author?

3. What is the Israeli national theater called?

4. Who was Shakespeare's famous Jewish character?

5. Who gave up T.V. stardom for a Chassidic lifestyle?

1. Richard Tucker
2. Arthur Miller
3. Habimah
4. Shylock
5. Steven Hill

1. Which Talmudic character slept for 70 years?

2. Which famous Jewish actor also races sports cars?

3. Which book club features the most Jewish children's titles each year?

4. Which Jewish actor was originally named Bernie Schwartz?

5. Why is Ron Blumberg of the Yankees in the Hall of Fame?

1. Honi Ha-meaggel
2. Paul Newman
3. The Enjoy-A-Book Club (over 100)
4. Tony Curtis
5. First designated hitter in major league baseball

1. Which 2 Jewish singers starred in the 2 versions of "The Jazz Singer"?

2. Which Jewish actor starred in "Spartacus"?

3. Who wrote the novel "Exodus"?

4. This Sabbath dish is affectionately called the "Jewish Soul Food"?

5. This language of European Jewry is comprised mainly of German and Hebrew?

1. Al Jolson and Neil Diamond
2. Kirk Douglas
3. Leon Uris
4. Cholent
5. Yiddish

1. This cigar-smoking comedian was married to Gracie Allen?

2. This famous Jewish comedian is famous for insulting people in the audience?

3. Who is the "Father of Television"?

4. This "Singing Rabbi" helped popularize modern Jewish music?

5. Who wrote "Heritage, Civilization and the Jews"?

1. George Burns
2. Don Rickles
3. Milton Berle
4. Shlomo Carlebach
5. Abba Eban

1. Name the Jewish heroes of Sir Walter Scott's "Ivanhoe"?

2. This famous composer wrote "West Side Story".

3. Who is the father of modern psychoanalysis?

4. What are the first names of the Gershwin brothers?

5. Who is the famous Jewish science fiction writer?

6. Who wrote "G-d Bless America"?

1. Rebecca and Isaac
2. Leonard Bernstein
3. Sigmund Freud
4. Ira and George
5. Isaac Asimov
6. Irving Berlin

CUSTOMS

AND

LAWS

1. Which liquid is forbidden by Jewish law to drink?

2. Why do we shake the Lulav in all directions?

3. Why do we have two challot on Shabbat?

4. When male children are blessed, what two names are usually used?

5. What is one reason that some Jews always wear a Yarmulka?

ANSWERS:

1. Blood
2. To show that G-d is everywhere
3. Because we received a double portion of mannah for every Shabbat in the desert.
4. Ephraim and Menassah
5. To remind us that G-d is always above us

1. What are the two characteristics of kosher seafood?

2. What are the fringes of the Tallit called?

3. What is the Shulchan Aruch called in English?

4. Which heavenly body is the Jewish calendar based on?

5. If a close relative dies, how long does one sit "Shivah"?

6. On which side of the doorpost is the mezuzah placed?

1. Fins and scales
2. Tzitzit
3. Code of Jewish Law
4. The moon
5. 7 days
6. Right

1. How often do the rabbis recommend checking a mezuzah parchment?

2. How old is a girl when she has a Bat Mitzvah?

3. The ark in the Synagogue faces in which direction?

4. What are the two characteristics of kosher, four-footed animals?

5. What is the blessing over the Challah?

6. In which prayer do we thank G-d for waking up?

1. Twice within each seven year period
2. 12 years old
3. East
4. Cloven hooves and chewing its cud
5. Hamotzi
6. Modeh Ani

1. What is the combined Mishnah and Gemarah called?

2. On which type of paper must the Torah be written?

3. What is a Tallit?

4. What was the Sanhedrin?

5. How many corners does a Tallit have?

6. What is the name of the special bread we eat on Shabbat?

1. Talmud
2. Parchment
3. A prayer shawl
4. The highest Jewish court of law — 120 members.
5. Four
6. Challah

1. Which two fabrics are forbidden to be woven together?

2. Which tribe served as Singers of the Psalms in The Temple?

3. Where does one wear tefillin?

4. What is read in the Synagogue on Monday, Thursday and Saturday?

5. The third meal on Shabbat is called _____?

6. How long does one mourn the death of a parent?

1. Wool and linen
2. Tribe of Levi
3. Head and Arm
4. The Torah
5. Shalosh Seudah
6. 12 months

1. What is the name of the prayer a mourner says?

2. Who writes mezuzahs and tefillin?

3. What is a "Siddur"?

4. Which Hebrew month comes twice during a leap year?

5. What are foods called that are neither meat nor dairy products?

6. Which blessing is said after eating bread?

1. Kaddish
2. A sofer — scribe
3. A prayer book
4. Adar
5. Parve
6. Birchat Hamazon

1. How many days are there in the Hebrew month?

2. Which letter is on the outside of the Mezuzah?

3. When does Shabbat begin?

1. 29 or 30 days
2. Shin
3. On Friday afternoon at sundown

HEBREW

LANGUAGE

1. What is the numerical value of the letter "kof"?

2. What does "Havdalah" mean?

3. What does "Shabbat" mean?

4. What does the word "Shofar" mean?

5. How do you say "Hebrew" in Hebrew?

6. The word "Tanach" is formed from the letter of which three Hebrew words?

1. What is another Hebrew word for the Torah?

2. The word "Synagogue" comes from which language?

3. What is Immigration to Israel called?

4. The Jews of Ethiopia are called Falashas. What does this mean?

5. What does "Seder" mean?

6. What is the "Galut"?

1. Chumash
2. Greek
3. Aliyah
4. Stranger or outcast
5. Order
6. Exile or the diaspora

1. What does "Lechem" mean?

2. What is the name of the Israeli Olympics?

3. What does "Chai" mean?

4. What does "Melech" mean?

5. In which direction is Hebrew written?

6. What does "Jerusalem" mean?

7. What does "Jaffa" mean?

1. Bread
2. Maccabee Games
3. Life or the number 18
4. King
5. Right to left
6. Dwelling of peace
7. Beautiful

1. What is the word for a collective farm in Israel?

2. What does the name "Ba'al Shem Tov" mean?

3. What is a "Get"?

4. Which Hebrew letters have no sound?

5. What is "Magen David Adom"?

6. What is the Hebrew word for "charity"?

1. Kibbutz
2. Master of the good name
3. A divorce
4. Aleph and Ayin
5. Jewish Red Cross
6. Tzedakah

1. What is the Hebrew word for circumcision?

2. What was the early name for the Land of Israel?

3. Name the Jewish months?

4. What does "Apocrypha" mean?

5. What does the word "Talmud" mean?

6. What part of the body is a "Shohk"?

1. Brit milah
2. Canaan
3. Tishrei, Cheshvan, Kislev, Tevet, Shevat, Adar, Nisan, Iyar, Sivan, Tamuz, Av, Elul.
4. Hidden Things
5. Study
6. Thigh

1. What is the name of the basic unit of money in Israel?

2. What is the name of Israel's elected parliament?

3. What does "Shammash" mean?

4. What does "El Al" mean?

5. How many final letters are there in the Hebrew language?

6. What is a "B'chor"?

1. Shekel
2. Knesset
3. Servant
4. Up in the air
5. 5
6. A first-born son

1. What is a "Mitzvah"?

2. Who was the Father of Modern Hebrew?

3. What is a native Israeli called?

4. What do you call songs sung on Shabbat?

5. What does the word "Minyan" mean?

6. The word for "President" in Hebrew is?

1. A good deed
2. Ben Yehudah
3. Sabra
4. Zemirot
5. Quorum of 10
6. Nasi

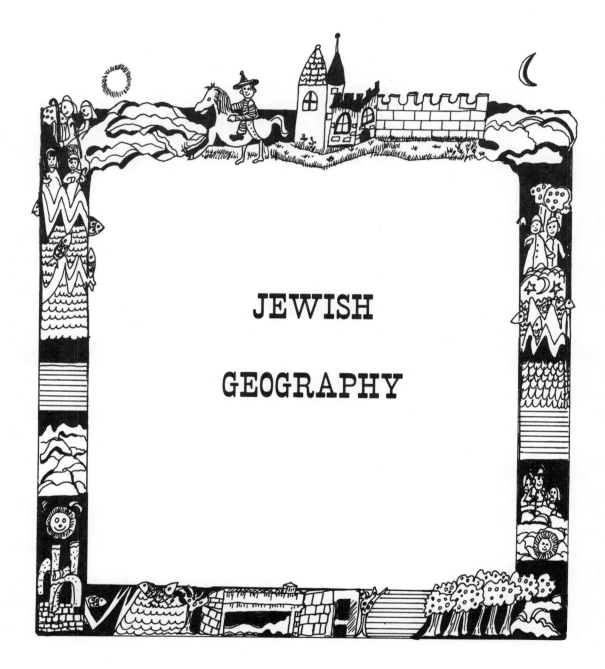

JEWISH

GEOGRAPHY

1. Which city is known as the "Gateway to the Negev"?

2. What are the mountains in the North of Israel called?

3. Israel is located on which continent?

4. Which modern day country was once Persia?

5. Where is the oldest synagogue in the Western Hemisphere?

1. Where is the lowest point on Earth?

2. Where was the Jewish Pale of Settlement?

3. How many provinces were in the Empire of Ahashverus?

4. What is the only fresh-water body of water in Israel today?

5. What is the name of the desert in South Israel?

1. The Dead Sea
2. Ukraine
3. 127
4. Sea of Galilee
5. Negev

1. In which city did the Arab terrorists murder the Israeli Olympic Athletes?

2. Where was the first Jewish ghetto?

3. What is the name of Israel's highest mountain?

4. What is the largest city in Israel?

5. What famous scrolls were found in Qumran?

1. Munich
2. Venice
3. Mount Meron
4. Tel Aviv
5. Dead Sea Scrolls

1. Which country is east of Israel?

2. What are the names of two major lakes in Israel?

3. What is the capital of Israel?

4. Which city has the largest Jewish population?

5. Which country refuses to release over 3,000,000 Jews?

6. What is the Biblical name for the West Bank?

1. Jordan
2. Kinneret and Dead Sea
3. Jerusalem
4. New York
5. Russia
6. Judea and Samaria

1. What country has the most Jews living in it now?

2. What is the most popular skiing area in Israel?

3. On how many hills is Jerusalem built?

4. How many wells was Be'er Sheva named for?

5. On which mountain is the city of Haifa built?

1. United States of America
2. Mount Hebron
3. 7
4. 7
5. Carmel

1. What is the name of the main airport in Israel?

2. Which fortress did Herod build?

3. What is the name of the largest port in Israel?

4. Which wall of the Temple remains standing?

5. Which Chinese city was famous for its Jews?

6. Which lake in Israel is shaped like a harp?

1. Ben Gurion Airport
2. Massada
3. Haifa
4. The Western Wall
5. Kai-Feng
6. Kinneret

1. Anne Frank's home is in which European city?

2. The Simon Wiesenthal Holocaust Center is located in which city?

3. In which country is the Auschwitz Concentration Camp located?

4. What is another name for the New York mountains called "The Borscht Belt"?

5. Where was the first permanent synagogue built in the United States?

1. Amsterdam
2. Los Angeles, California
3. Poland
4. The Catskill Mountains
5. Newport, Rhode Island

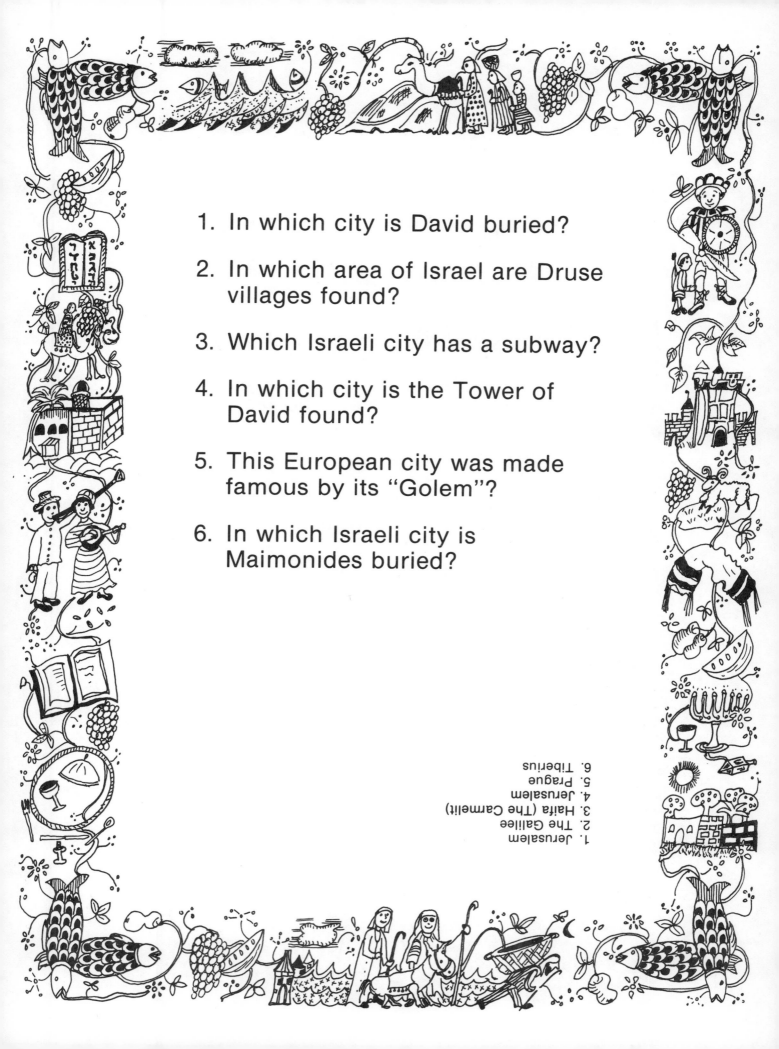

1. In which city is David buried?

2. In which area of Israel are Druse villages found?

3. Which Israeli city has a subway?

4. In which city is the Tower of David found?

5. This European city was made famous by its "Golem"?

6. In which Israeli city is Maimonides buried?

1. Jerusalem
2. The Galilee
3. Haifa (The Carmelit)
4. Jerusalem
5. Prague
6. Tiberius

1. Which major area of Israel was returned to Egypt under the Camp David Accord?

2. In which famous valley did Joshua stop the sun?

3. At which mountain did Deborah and Barak defeat the enemies of Israel?

4. Throughout history in which Israeli city was Kaballah studied?

5. Which country had the largest population of Jews until 1492?

1. Sinai
2. Ayalon
3. Mt. Tabor
4. Safed
5. Spain

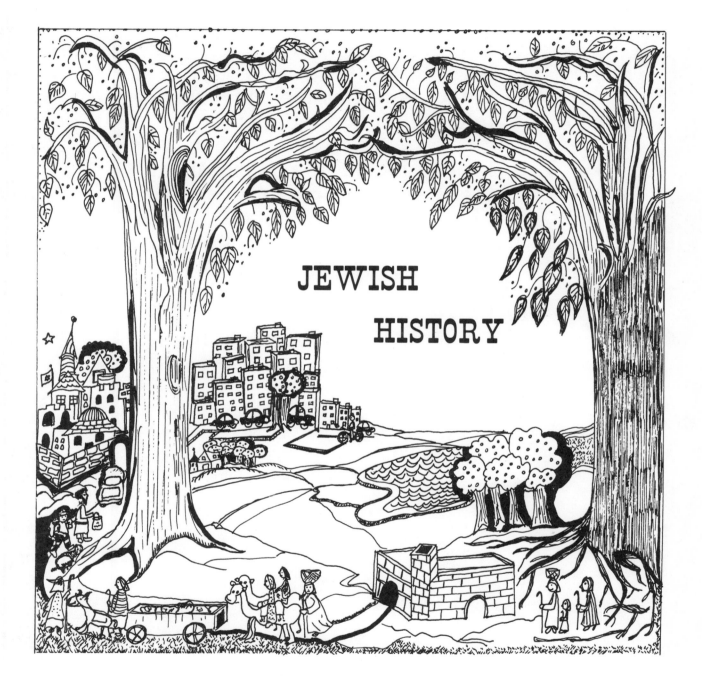

JEWISH

HISTORY

1. Which rabbi was known to never become angry?

2. Onkolos translated the Torah into which language?

3. From which Tribe of Israel will the Messiah come?

4. Where did the Israelites find the blue color for their tzitzit?

5. Name two foods which the rabbis felt were possibly the "forbidden fruits" of the tree of knowledge?

1. Which war did Israel fight in 1967?

2. Name the girl whose diary has become standard reading about the Holocaust?

3. Where did Bar Kochba make his last stand?

4. What was the first Greek translation of the Bible called?

5. Who were the "secret Jews" of the Spanish Inquisition?

1. The Six Day War
2. Anne Frank
3. Betar
4. The Septuagint
5. The Marranos

1. Who toppled the Temple of Dagon?

2. What were the dying words of Rabbi Akiba?

3. In which year was the final expulsion of the Jews from Spain?

4. What great rabbi has a sandwich named after him?

5. Which war did Israel fight in 1973?

1. Operation "Magic Carpet" saved the Jews of which country?

2. Who forbade polygamy for the Jews?

3. Which cities did the Israelites build in Egypt?

4. Who was the editor of the Mishnah?

5. Who introduced the first Jewish mathematical and astronomical calendar?

1. Which revolt took place in 135 C.E.?

2. When was the second Temple destroyed?

3. In which year did Israel become a state?

4. What are the colors of the Israeli flag?

5. When was the first Temple destroyed?

6. The walls of which city fell when Joshua blew the trumpets?

6. Jericho
5. 597 B.C.E.
4. Blue and white
3. 1948
2. 70 C.E.
1. Bar Kochba

1. Who was the Israeli ambassador to the U.S. from 1950-1955?

2. Where was Moses Maimonides born?

3. In modern Israel, which group worships on Mt. Gerizim?

4. Of which underground Jewish army was Menachem Begin commander?

5. Jewish hostages were rescued from the airport in which African city?

1. Abba Eban
2. Cordoba, Spain
3. Shomronim
4. The Irgun
5. Entebbe

1. What is the name of the historical treaty between Jimmy Carter, Menachem Begin and Anwar Sadat?

2. Which of Jerusalem's gates is named after a Jewish King?

3. Which city in China became home to many Jewish refugees during World War II?

4. Who wrote the Kuzari?

5. This Polish ghetto became the symbol of Jewish resistance in W.W.II?

1. The Camp David Accords
2. Herod's Gate
3. Shanghai
4. Yehudah HaLevi
5. Warsaw

1. Which Jew created the "Russian Red Army"?

2. This movement brought secular learning to the Jews of Europe?

3. Which country forced Jewish children to serve in their army?

4. This document, in 1914, promised the Jews their own homeland.

5. What is the name of the elite fighting force of the Hagganah?

1. Leon Trotsky
2. Enlightenment (Haskalah)
3. Russia
4. Balfour Declaration
5. Palmach

1. In which year did Israel leave Lebanon?

2. What was the currency used by Israel before the Shekel?

3. Who ruled Palestine before the British?

4. Which country has the largest arsenal of captured Russian weapons?

5. What is the most famous Israeli weapon?

1. 1985
2. Lira
3. The Turks
4. Israel
5. UZI — sub-machine gun

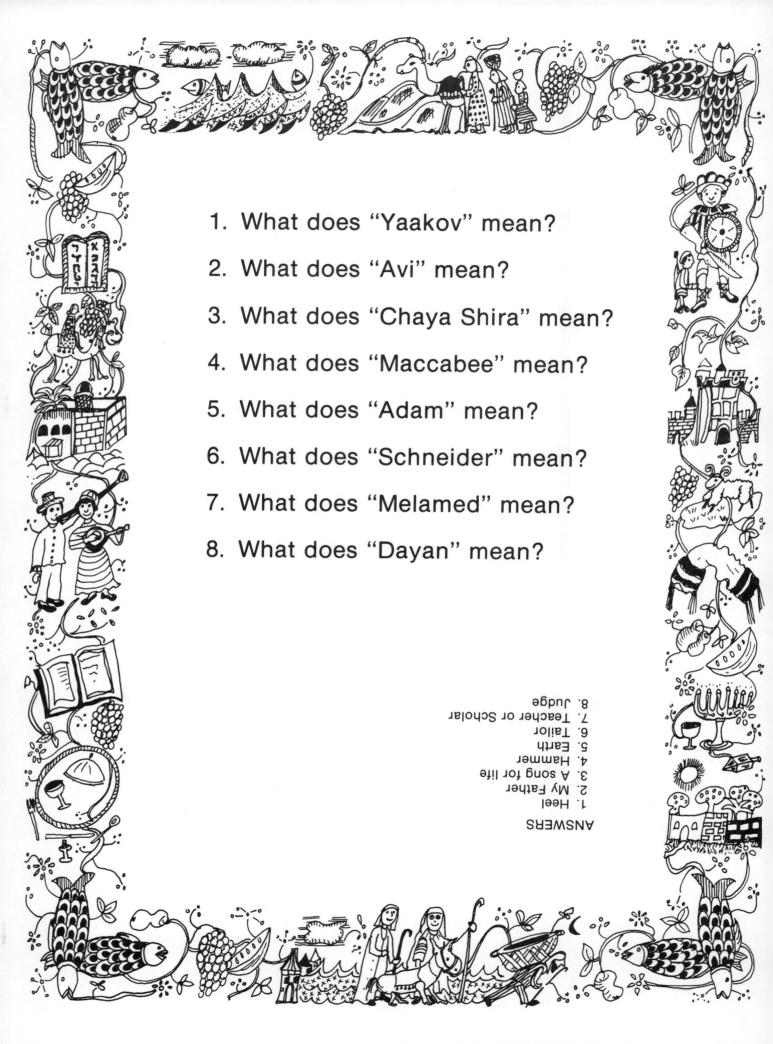

1. What does "Yaakov" mean?

2. What does "Avi" mean?

3. What does "Chaya Shira" mean?

4. What does "Maccabee" mean?

5. What does "Adam" mean?

6. What does "Schneider" mean?

7. What does "Melamed" mean?

8. What does "Dayan" mean?

ANSWERS

1. Heel
2. My Father
3. A song for life
4. Hammer
5. Earth
6. Tailor
7. Teacher or Scholar
8. Judge

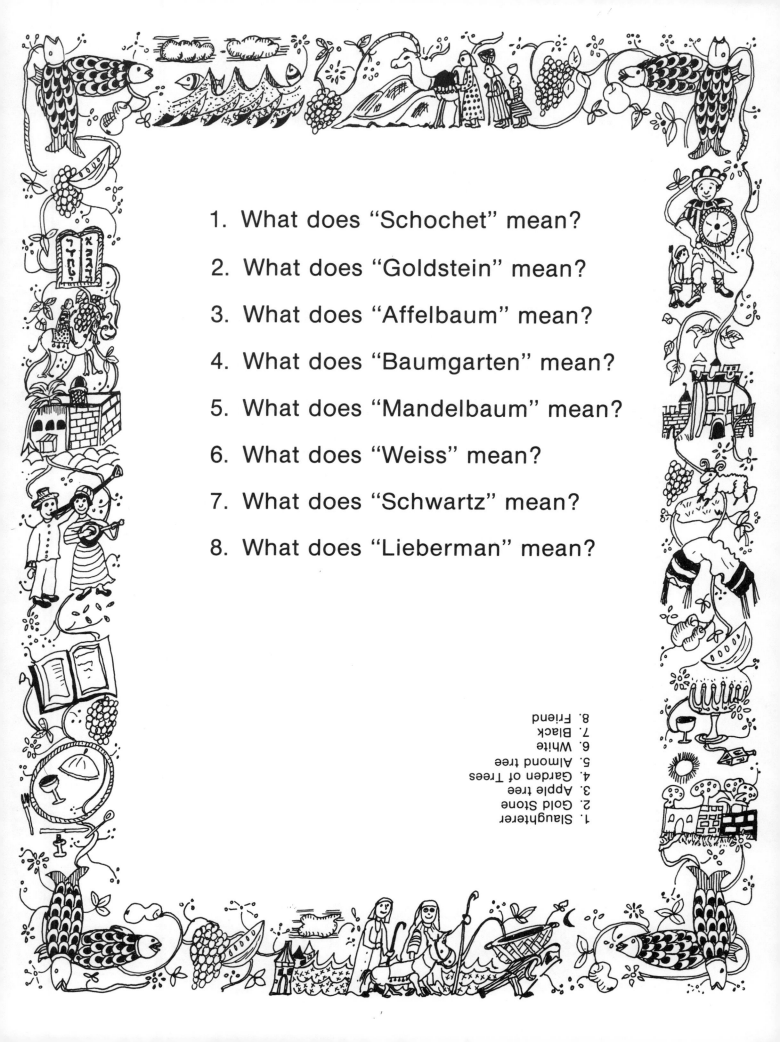

1. What does "Schochet" mean?

2. What does "Goldstein" mean?

3. What does "Affelbaum" mean?

4. What does "Baumgarten" mean?

5. What does "Mandelbaum" mean?

6. What does "Weiss" mean?

7. What does "Schwartz" mean?

8. What does "Lieberman" mean?

1. Slaughterer
2. Gold Stone
3. Apple tree
4. Garden of Trees
5. Almond tree
6. White
7. Black
8. Friend

1. What does "Isaac" mean?

2. What does "Jeremiah" mean?

3. What does "Raphael" mean?

4. What does "Michael" mean?

5. What does "Abigail" mean?

6. What does "Solomon" mean?

7. What does "Joshua" mean?

8. What does "Hadassah" mean?

1. He laughs
2. G-d exalts
3. G-d has healed
4. Who is like G-d
5. My father is joyous
6. Peaceable
7. G-d saves
8. Myrtle tree

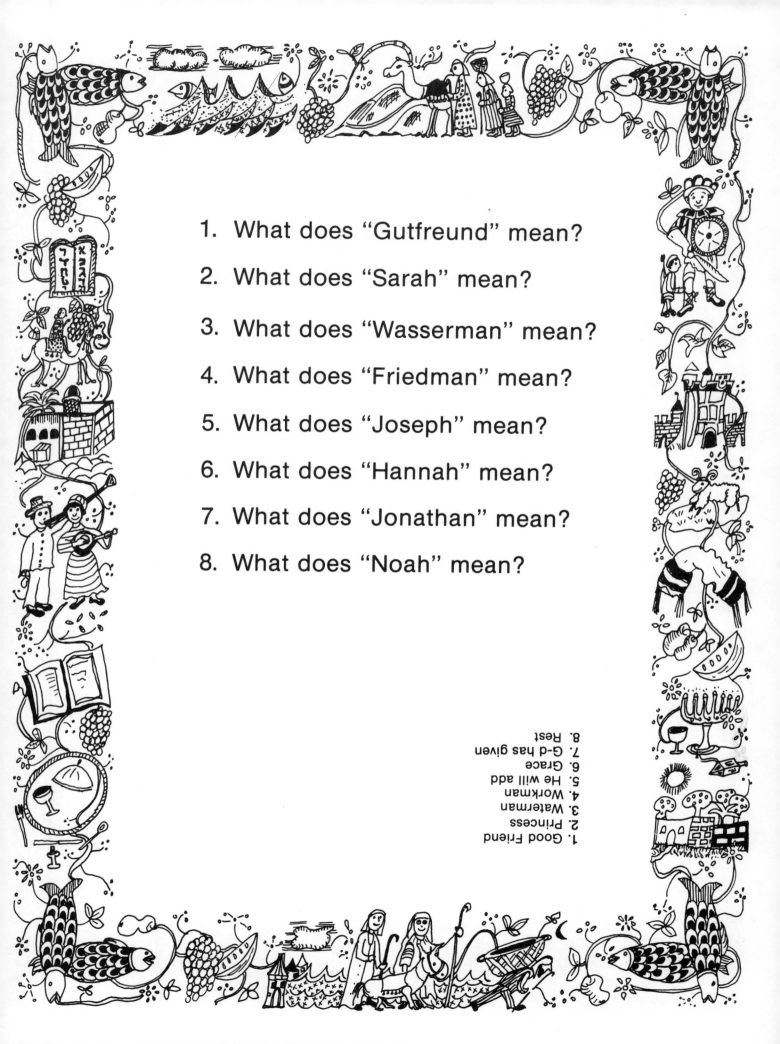

1. What does "Gutfreund" mean?

2. What does "Sarah" mean?

3. What does "Wasserman" mean?

4. What does "Friedman" mean?

5. What does "Joseph" mean?

6. What does "Hannah" mean?

7. What does "Jonathan" mean?

8. What does "Noah" mean?

1. Good Friend
2. Princess
3. Waterman
4. Workman
5. He will add
6. Grace
7. G-d has given
8. Rest

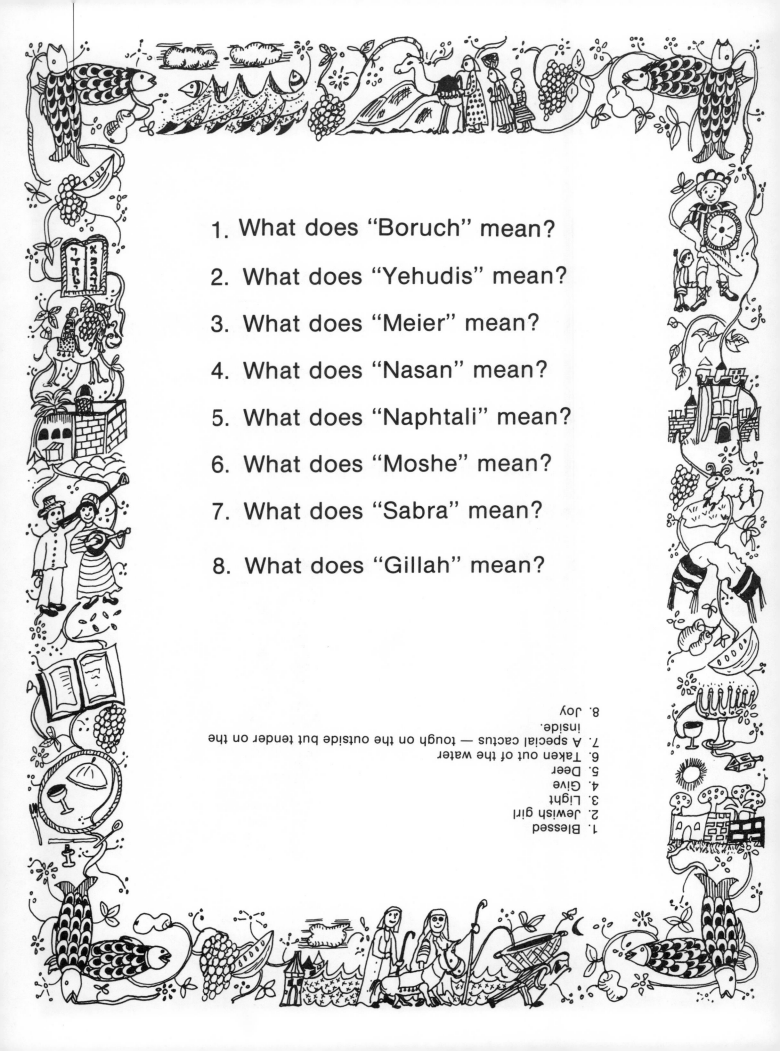

1. What does "Boruch" mean?

2. What does "Yehudis" mean?

3. What does "Meier" mean?

4. What does "Nasan" mean?

5. What does "Naphtali" mean?

6. What does "Moshe" mean?

7. What does "Sabra" mean?

8. What does "Gillah" mean?

1. Blessed
2. Jewish girl
3. Light
4. Give
5. Deer
6. Taken out of the water
7. A special cactus — tough on the outside but tender on the inside.
8. Joy